HEINEMANN MATHEMATICS 1

Name

WORKBOOK 5

Addition to 6

Revised

How many fish?

Put fish in the jars.

2 and 1 ⟶ ☐

1 and 3 ⟶ ☐

3 and 2 ⟶ ☐

4 and 2 ⟶ ☐

3 and 3 ⟶ ☐

Girls and boys

Put in

5 girls	2 boys	⟶ ☐ altogether
5 girls	5 boys	⟶ ☐ altogether
3 girls	6 boys	⟶ ☐ altogether
2 girls	6 boys	⟶ ☐ altogether

Girls and boys

3 and 3 → ☐

☐ and ☐ → ☐

☐ and ☐ → ☐

☐ and ☐ → ☐

☐ and ☐ → ☐

☐ and ☐ → ☐

Draw and add.

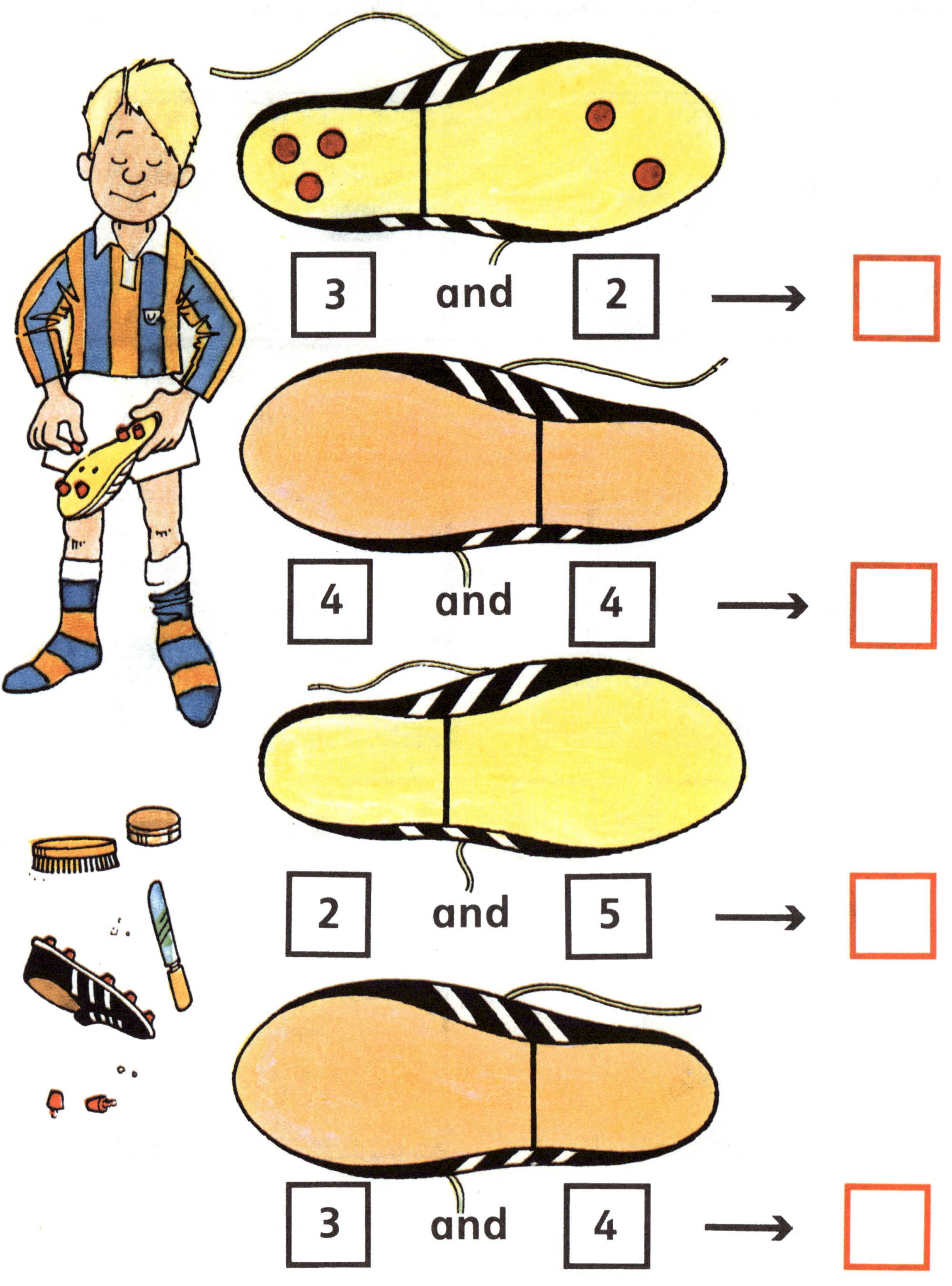

How many altogether?

Peas

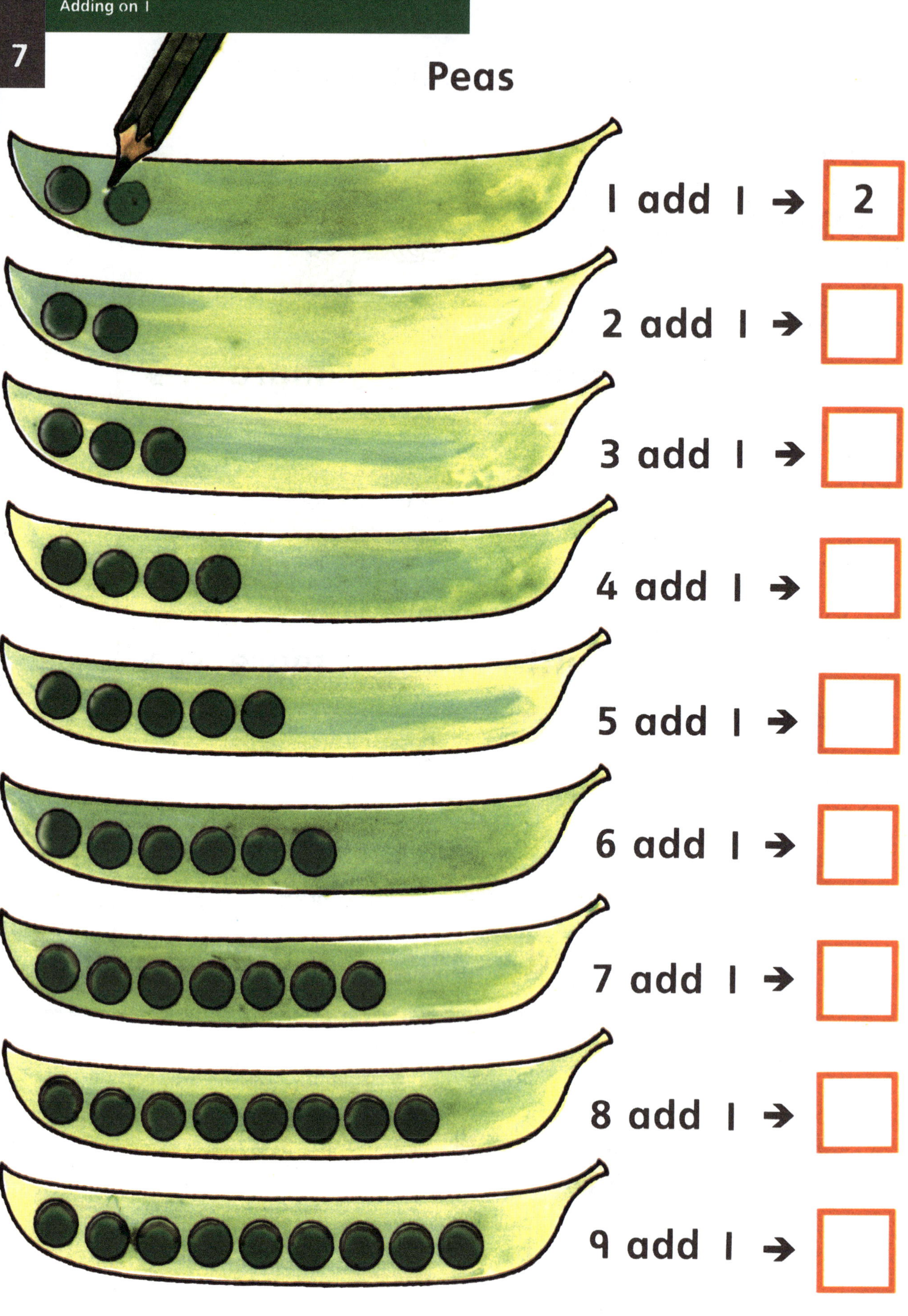

Ice cubes

Put in 6  .
Add 2.

6 add 2 → ☐

Put in 3  .
Add 2.

3 add 2 → ☐

1 add 2 ⟶ ☐   5 add 2 ⟶ ☐

2 add 2 ⟶ ☐   6 add 2 ⟶ ☐

3 add 2 ⟶ ☐   7 add 2 ⟶ ☐

4 add 2 ⟶ ☐   8 add 2 ⟶ ☐

R1

Adding 1 or 2

Adding 1 or 2

3   +   1   → ☐

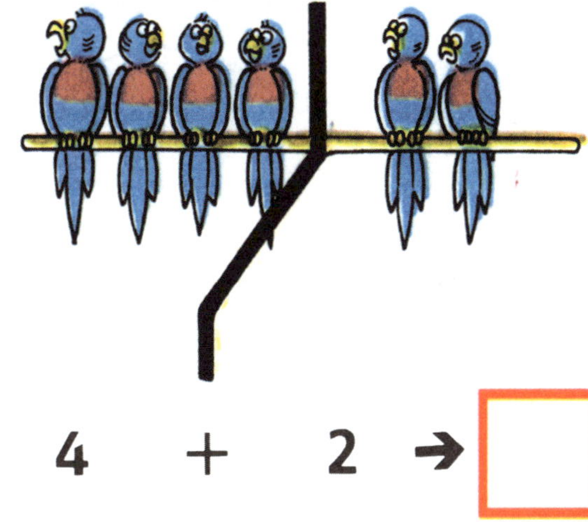

4   +   2   → ☐

5   +   1   = ☐

2   +   ☐   = ☐

☐   +   ☐   = ☐

☐   +   ☐   = ☐

Put 4 spots on the monster.

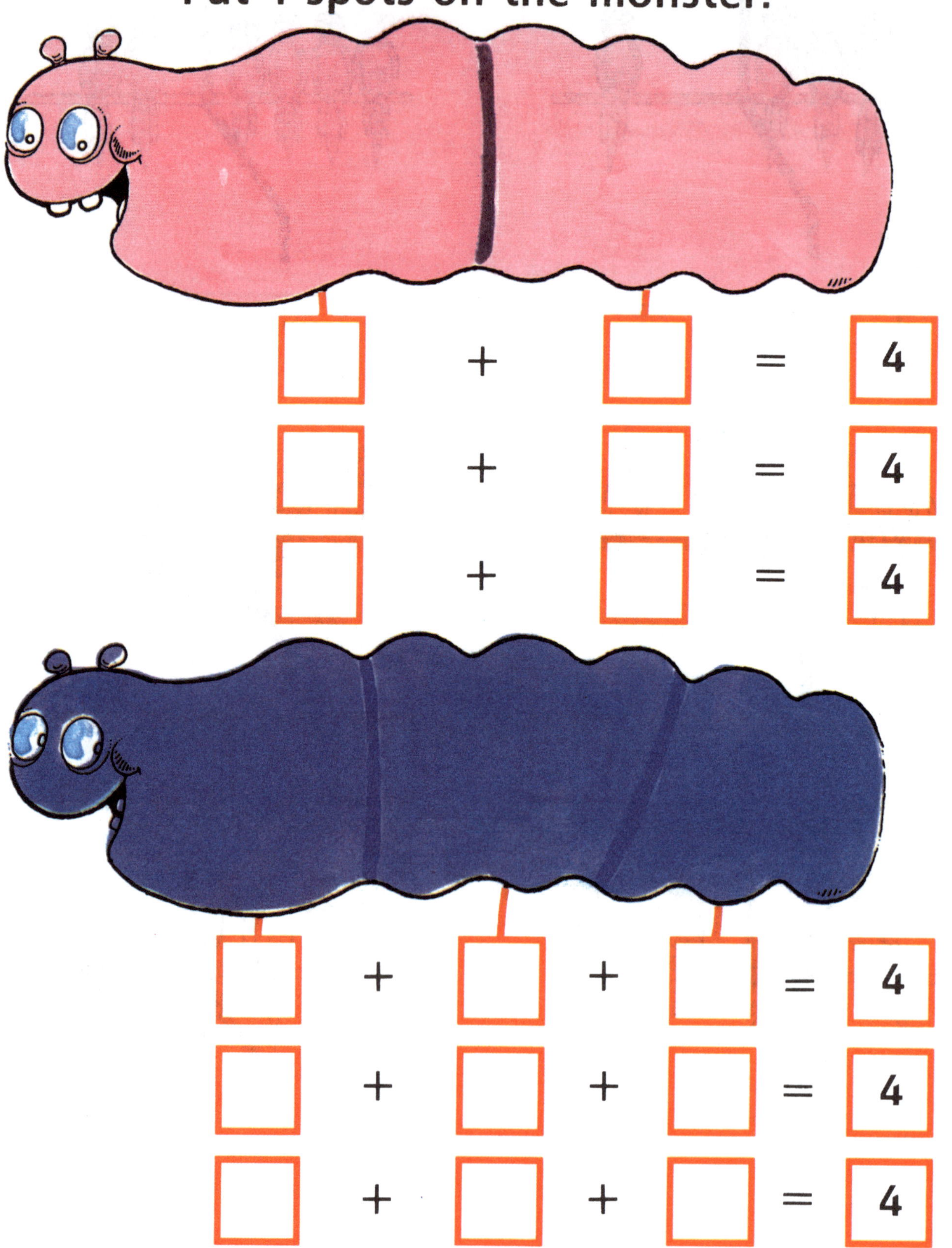

Draw spots.

Put in 5 parcels.

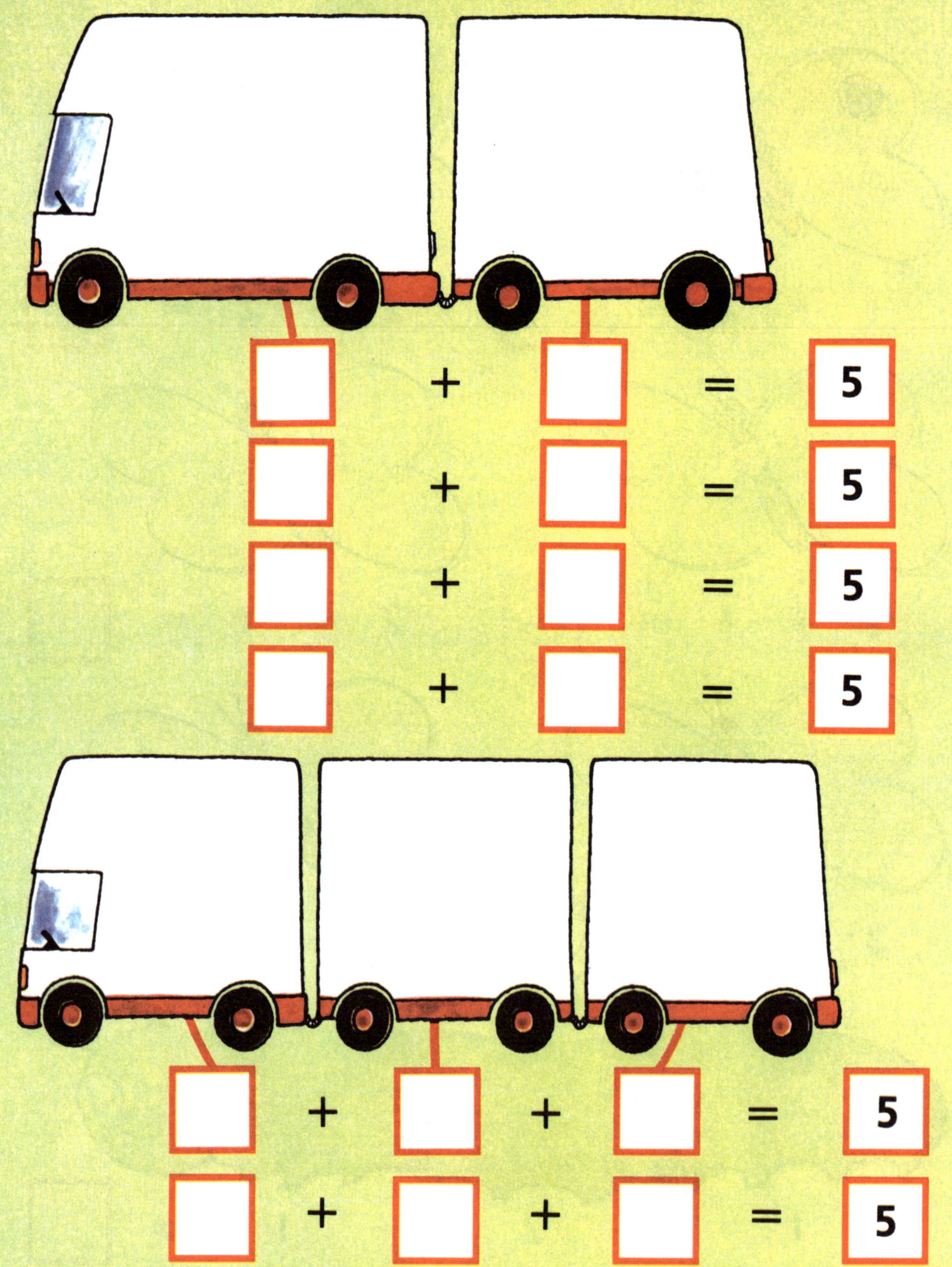

Draw and add.

3 + 1 =

4 + 1 =

3 + 2 =

2 + 3 =

2 + 2 =

1 + 4 =

1 + 3 =

2 + 3 =

R2

Count and add.

Spots

Monday

$$1 + 5 = 6$$

Tuesday

$$2 + 4 =$$

Wednesday

$$3 +$$

Thursday

Friday

Saturday

R3

Moves

Start here

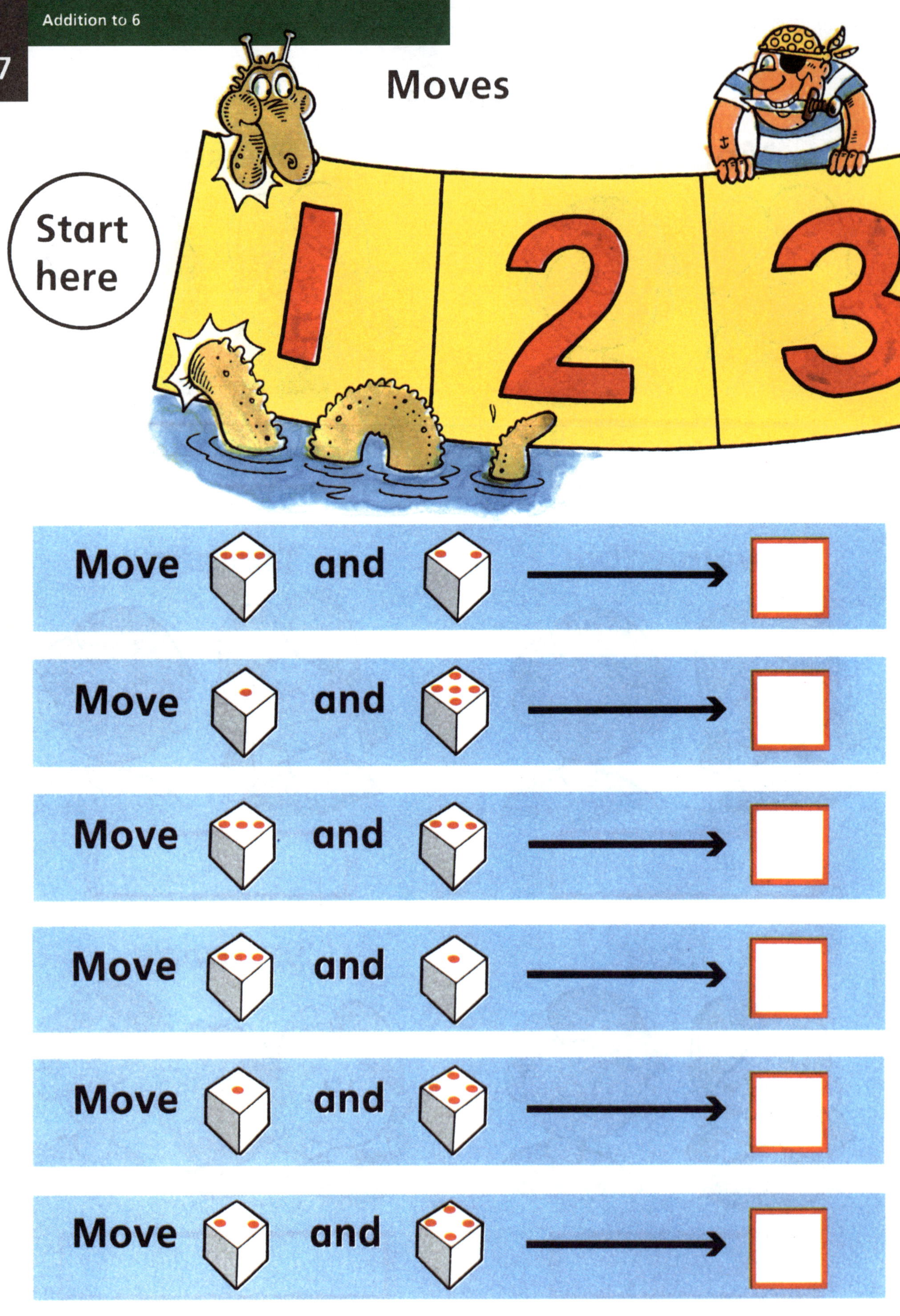

4 5 6

4 + 1 =

Draw dots.

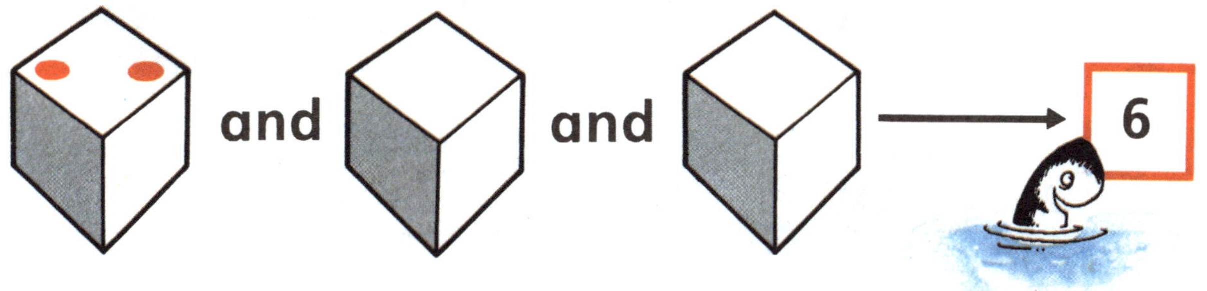

Sam's Sweets

Buy	1p	and	2p	
Buy	2p	and	3p	
Buy	3p	and	3p	
Buy	1p	and	2p	
Buy	3p	and	2p	
Buy	2p	and	2p	

Make each **1p** more.

Pets

$2 + 1 =$ ☐

$1 + 2 =$ ☐

$3 + 1 =$ ☐

$1 + 3 =$ ☐

$4 + 1 =$ ☐

$1 + 4 =$ ☐

$3 + 2 =$ ☐

$2 + 3 =$ ☐

$5 + 1 =$ ☐

$1 + 5 =$ ☐

$4 + 2 =$ ☐

$2 + 4 =$ ☐

How many?

on the bridge ☐

under the bridge ☐

altogether ☐

on the branch ☐

under the branch ☐

altogether ☐

on the rope ☐

under the rope ☐

altogether ☐

on the desk ☐

under the desk ☐

altogether ☐

1	2	3	4	5	6	7	8	9	10	11	12	13	14	15	16	17	18	19	20	21	22	23

Heinemann is an imprint of Pearson Education Limited, a company incorporated in England and Wales, having its registered office at Edinburgh Gate, Harlow, Essex, CM20 2JE.
Registered company number: 872828
ISBN 978 0 435 03086 5 © Scottish Primary Mathematics Group 1991.
First published 1991. Revised edition 1995.   21   30
Typeset and illustrated by Oxprint Design. Printed and bound in Great Britain by Bell and Bain Ltd, Glasgow